Primrose's Woodland Adventure Sticker Book

Join Primrose as she makes
some new woodland fairy friends!
Use the stickers on each page to add
to the beautiful Flower Fairy scenes.

Inspired by life with the Flower Fairies
With illustrations by Cicely Mary Barker
FREDERICK WARNE

A New Day

A shy Flower Fairy, Primrose often stays tucked away underneath trees where she feels safe and cosy. Today Primrose wants to do something new. Dare she set out to explore the nearby woodland?

Add some Flower
Fairies to this scene.
Some fairies live high up in
the treetops, whilst others
prefer the shady woodland floor.
Add some flowers, too!

High in the Sky

"Come up here and play with us," Elder calls to Primrose. Up above, fairies swing in the branches. White Bryony tells Primrose she'll show her how to make pretty garlands. Poplar asks Primrose if she wants to play a game of 'catch' with one of his balls of fluff!

In the treetops other Flower Fairies watch the fun and games. Primrose can hear them talking and laughing but she can't see where they all are. Colourful blossom and berries adorn the high branches of the trees.

Add more Flower Fairies and decorate these pages with nuts, berries and pine cones.

A Song and Dance

As Primrose wanders further into the woodland she hears singing. There are Flower Fairies dancing amongst the trees!

Almond Blossom dances along her branch and Ash Tree skips along daintily to the music. Lilac blows some of her sweet fragrance to scent the air.

"Come and join us," they say to Primrose, but she is too shy. Some Flower Fairies love to sing or dance and skip. Others, such as Primrose, prefer to watch the merriment.

Add little Pear Blossom
and dancing Columbine.
Then stick in lots of musical
instruments so that all the
fairies can join in the fun!

First Flight

Primrose hears some nervous giggling. In a secluded glade she finds some Flower Fairy toddlers practising their flying skills.

Baby Apple Blossom is summoning up her courage, while Spindle Berry makes a crash landing into one of her branches.

"Can I try?" asks young Guelder Rose, who thinks flying looks much more fun than walking!

Pages 2-3
Pages 4-5
Pages 6-7
Pages 8-9

Pages 10-11
Pages 12-13
Pages 14-15
Page 16

Add Lavender and Harebell,
then stick in some branches,
leaves and soft flowers
for the young fairies
to land on.

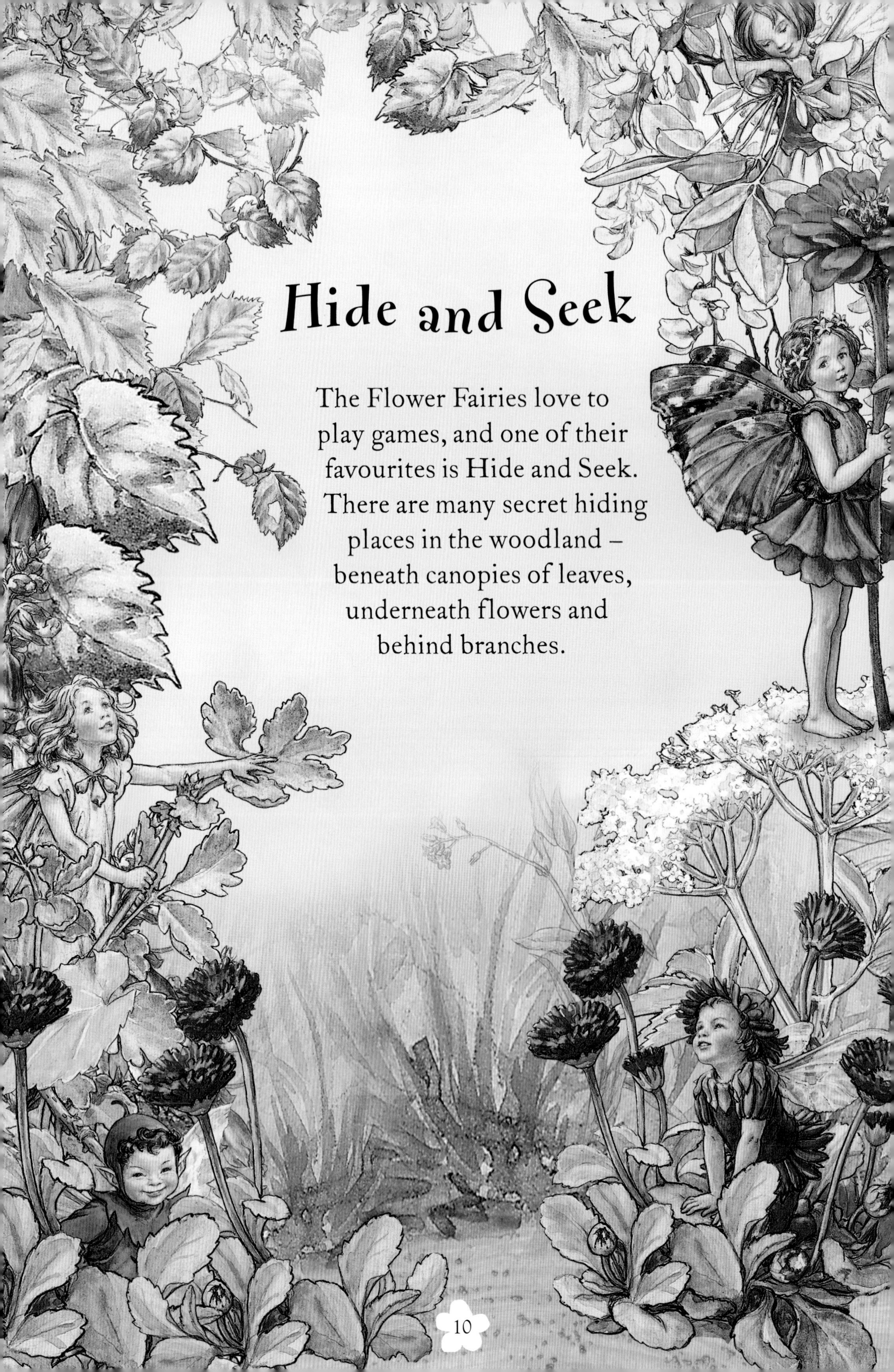

Hide and Seek

The Flower Fairies love to play games, and one of their favourites is Hide and Seek. There are many secret hiding places in the woodland – beneath canopies of leaves, underneath flowers and behind branches.

"Help me find where the others are hiding!" Laburnum calls to Primrose.

Bees and a butterfly join in the fun, and are clever at finding well-hidden fairies!

Use leaves and flowers to cover more of the fairies so they can play hide and seek!

A Perfect Picnic

Primrose can't wait to tell all her friends about the wonderful things happening in the woodland. "Let's have a picnic" says Narcissus. She thinks Primrose must be hungry after her adventure. Mountain Ash and Acorn can hardly wait to hear what Primrose has been doing!

Sweet Chestnut throws down some nuts for the fairies to eat, and Blackberry gives some of her juiciest berries for the picnic. From Elder there's delicious elderflower cordial.

Add some more Flower Fairies to this happy scene, then stick on some tasty treats too.

Primrose's Party

Primrose's picnic turns into a party. All the Flower Fairies want to come, and they bring gifts from meadow, garden, hedgerow and woodland. Soon the glade is covered with fairy decorations, and there are Flower Fairies everywhere!

Primrose wonders why she was so shy. In one day, she's made lots of new friends. She can see them all around her – on the ground and high up in the treetops!

Decorate this lovely picture with lanterns and garlands, then add more fairies. Everyone would like to come to Primrose's party!

Goodnight, Fairies!

What an exciting day it's been for Primrose! She's explored new parts of Flower Fairyland and met lots of new friends. Now as the stars fill the sky it's time for all the Flower Fairies to curl up under their petals and go to sleep. Who knows what adventures tomorrow will hold?

Stick sleepy fairies to the page, and make sure they all have somewhere soft and cosy to rest.